HOW TO USE . . . *This Manual*

Getting the Best out of the Bible is designed to help you gain an understanding of one of the most important principles of Christian living — Biblical Meditation. This is probably one of the least understood and the most neglected of all spiritual disciplines. And when one considers how much God promises to those who meditate, it is time we took a new look at this vitally important subject.

This manual is essentially a workbook — to be used rather than just read and then put on your bookshelf. It can be used individually or by a group. It is important to cover one section at a time. Make sure that you understand what is being said before going on to the next section. Don't skip the questions or exercises. These are designed not only to help you comprehend each section but to open up your mind and spirit to the truth of God's Word.

It must be pointed out at the beginning that meditation is not a "cure all" for everything. It should not be seen as a substitute for other spiritual disciplines nor as a way of escape from one's responsibilities. Those who benefit most from meditation in the Scriptures are those who are obedient to them. When glaring violations of scripture are allowed to go on uncorrected in a person's life, no matter how much that person tries to meditate, the Bible will remain a closed book.

That does not mean you have to be perfect in order to discover the rewards of meditation, but it does mean you have to have a willing and an obedient heart. Throughout the ages the people of God have discovered that the more one obeys the Word of God the more light shines out from it.

I pray that as you use this manual you will go on to experience a dimension of Christian life and experience that you might never before have touched. Believe me, the hours you spend in reading *and* meditating on the Scriptures will become the most profitable hours of your life.

Selwyn Hughes

1

Biblical Meditation is the process of holding a phrase or verse of Scripture in the mind, pondering it, continually contemplating it, dwelling upon it, viewing it from every angle of the imagination, until it begins to affect the deepest parts of one's spiritual being.

Andrew Murray defined meditation as "holding the Word of God in the mind until it has affected every area of one's life and character". Campbell McAlpine says, "Meditation is the devotional practice of pondering the words of a verse, or verses of Scripture, with a receptive heart, allowing the Holy Spirit to take the written Word and apply it as the living word to the inner being". And Bill Gothard, an American Bible teacher, likens the process of meditation to a person slowly turning a many faceted diamond in the light to feast upon its beauty from every possible angle.

The word 'meditate' or 'meditation' can be found in many parts of the Bible. A study of some of the passages in which the word is found and the original Hebrew or Greek word that is used gives a clue to its rich and varied meaning.

Psalm 1:2

". . . on his law he *meditates* day and night"
The word used here is *hagah* which means to murmur (in pleasure), to ponder. Meditation is a pleasant 'murmuring' of Scripture to oneself.

Psalm 119:99

". . . for I *meditate* on your statutes".
The word used here is *sichah* which means to reflect with deep devotion; to contemplate. Meditation is the quiet contemplation of and reflection on Scripture.

Psalm 19:14

"May the words of my mouth and the *meditation* of my heart be pleasing in your sight O Lord . . ."
The word used here is *higgayon* which means a musical notation, a murmuring sound. Meditation is a musical repetition of God's Word.

1 Timothy 4:15   "*Meditate* upon these things . . ." (KJV)

The word used here is *meletao* which means to ponder carefully with the mind; to muse upon. Meditation is a careful and prayerful reviewing of Scripture.

The deep meaning that lies beneath the word 'meditate' as used in Scripture can be best understood by observing what happens in the digestive system of ruminant animals. These are animals such as sheep, goats, camels, cows and giraffes which 'chew the cud'. The way a ruminant animal digests its food is fascinating.

First, it literally bolts its food down, and then later regurgitates it out of its stomach back into its mouth. It does this several times, a process which enables the food to be thoroughly digested, whereupon it is absorbed into the animal's bloodstream, so becoming part of its life.

Rumination and meditation are parallel words. When a Christian takes a phrase or verse of Scripture and begins to meditate upon it the power that is resident in God's Word is absorbed into one's inner being, producing spiritual energy and faith.

Just as a ruminant animal gets its nourishment and energy from what it eats and by the process of regurgitation, so a Christian who meditates extracts from the Scriptures the life of God which it contains. Meditation, therefore, is the digestive system of the soul.

BASED ON WHAT YOU HAVE READ SO FAR
GIVE IN YOUR OWN WORDS A DEFINITION OF
MEDITATION . . .

Meditation is _____

_____

_____

_____

_____

"But his delight is in the Law of the Lord . . . night and day"

There are many forms of meditation practised in today's world. The most popular is Transcendental Meditation, or 'TM'. This approach to meditation, made popular by an Indian mystic, Maharishi Mahesh Yogi, is expanding rapidly throughout western society. "TM", said the Maharishi, "is a form of prayer and a path to God." He claims that by stilling the mind and stopping all perception and thought, one merges with the universe and experiences 'transcendence' by making contact with God who is described as the impersonal "All".

Here are some more words of the Maharishi Mahesh Yogi which show at once how the whole system is diametrically opposite to God's revelation of Himself in the Scriptures:

> The practice of Transcendental Meditation unfolds the full potential of the divine in man, and brings human consciousness to the level of God consciousness . . . A most refined and powerful form of prayer is this meditation, which leads us to the field of the Creator, to the sources of Creation, to the field of God.

The experience of 'transcendence', of being lifted up to God, is illusory and unbiblical. If putting one's thoughts into neutral enables a person to climb up to God then the Incarnation of Jesus Christ was unnecessary and unimportant. Transcendental Meditation, in its effort to help people get to know God, by-passes Jesus Christ. Any system of religion that seeks to do that is anti-Christ.

'TM' also adopts the position that man holds within his being the answer to his own destiny. It fails to recognise that "all have sinned and fall short of the glory of God" (Rom. 3:23) and that our fallen human nature has a bias that will lead us away from God rather than toward Him.

TRANSCENDENTAL MEDITATION	BIBLICAL MEDITATION
Seeks to empty the mind of all activity and thought.	Seeks to fill the mind with thoughts of God (Matt. 22:37).
Can open the personality to unknown spiritual forces.	Teaches man to be alert to the activity of evil spiritual forces (Eph. 6:12).
Focuses on bringing man to God.	Focuses on how God comes to man (Col. 2:9).
Encourages a belief in self-dependency.	Encourages a belief in God-dependency (John 15:5).
Says that man's greatest sin is that he is ignorant of the fact that he is divine.	Proclaims that the way to God is through Christ alone (John 14:6).
Believes that man can overcome sin by meditation.	Focuses on the blood of Christ for the expiation of sin (1 John 1:7).
Says that the answer to every problem is that there is no problem.	Encourages a dependence on Christ for spiritual strength (Matt. 11:28).
Involves worship of a *deceased guru* — Guru Dev.	Concentrates on the one living God (Acts 2:32).
Recognises a number of gods in using the mantra.	Declares one God, in the first biblical commandment (Ex. 20:3).
Claims that the key to the fulfilment of every religion is found in the regular practice of TM.	Affirms that there is one mediator between God and man — Christ Jesus (1 Tim. 2:5).

In his book *The Practice of Biblical Meditation* (Marshalls),
Campbell McAlpine writes:

> ❝ A friend of ours, Tryna, who had been involved in transcendental meditation before she came to know the Lord Jesus in a personal way, had this to say:
>
> We used to descend down into ourselves, firmly and consistently pushing away all distracting thoughts. Our goal was to arrive at a state of nothingness, which we called peace. I would settle down into a void of blackness, a darkness which could be felt.
>
> What a difference biblical meditation has brought to my life. Here God's Word is the focus instead of self; satisfaction instead of emptiness; insight instead of darkness. Here was revelation from God instead of another mystical experience.
>
> I found power in God's Word to heal me and cleanse my mind, feed and satisfy my soul, and strengthen my spirit. Revelation 3:20 became especially meaningful: 'If any man hear my voice and open the door, I will come in to him, and sup with him and he with me.' I learned to hear God's voice. ❞

CONSIDER:

1. What do you think are the fundamental mistakes in the views behind transcendental meditation?
2. A friend or work colleague tells you that they are thinking of attending a course in TM. What would you say to them?

2

Many Christians believe that to get the best out of the Bible they simply have to read it and study it. The truth is however that while reading and studying the Bible are important spiritual disciplines we will not get the best out of God's Word until we learn how to meditate in it.

The words of God which are recorded in Scripture are living words containing inexhaustible power and wisdom. One writer describes them as "eternal wisdom within the shell of human words". Through meditation we can 'break open' these human words and discover something of the deep wisdom and understanding that lies within them. Christians who have followed Christ for many years and have a long experience in studying the Scriptures are constantly amazed at the rewards of meditation. They find new light breaking forth from a verse or passage of Scripture which hitherto they thought they clearly understood.

Reading, studying and memorising the Bible are largely intellectual exercises which feed the mind and ultimately the spirit. Meditation, however, takes what has been fed into the mind and more effectively presses its truth and power deep into the spirit where it can bring about the greatest results.

To understand this concept one must see the difference between the mind and the spirit. The Bible says that there are three parts to our being — spirit, soul and body (1 Thess. 5:23). Some Christians believe that the terms 'spirit' and 'soul' are interchangeable and therefore apply to the same thing, but it is clear from Hebrews 4:12 that there is a division betwen the spirit and soul.

The spirit is the centre of our personality, the motivating point of our whole being. The Bible sometimes refers to this part of our personalities as the 'heart'. The soul is that part of us which contains our mind (or thoughts), our feelings (or emotions) and our will (our decisions).

When we read, study and memorise the Bible the action begins in our mind and eventually passes through the mind into the spirit, where it affects the deep springs of our being. When we meditate however, (i.e. ponder, contemplate and reflect on a text or phrase) the Word of God is pressed more speedily, more effectively and more deeply into the spiritual part of our being.

We have three drives — spiritual, psychological (soul) and physical. God designed us so that the spiritual part of us is the most important and most powerful. This is how Christ lived when He was here upon earth. His psychological and physical drives were under the control of His spirit. When this happens the personality experiences inner balance.

In Psalm 4:4 we read:

"Meditate in your heart upon your bed and be still" (NASB).

This helps to clarify even further what meditation is all about. It is passing the word of God between the mind and the spirit (or heart) backwards and forwards, over and over again, until its cleansing and healing power permeates and penetrates the deepest parts of our being. The action of prayerfully holding a scriptural thought in the mind, talking to oneself about it, drawing every drop of spiritual nourishment from it, has a dynamic and powerful spiritual effect upon the personality.

Simply to hold a text in the mind as an exercise of memory and not meditate on it (i.e. draw from it the spiritual nourishment it contains) is rather like swallowing a sweet without sucking it. How much more tasteful and digestible it is when it is placed on the tip of the tongue and its delights are more leisurely and lengthily enjoyed.

TAKE A MOMENT TO EVALUATE this section and give three reasons of your own why meditation is so important.

Meditation is important because:

1. _____

2. _____

3. _____

Door to Discovery

"Meditation" says A.T. Pierson, "is simply thought prolonged and directed to a single object". Those who have made great scientific discoveries have proved this to be true.

M.A. Rosanoff, for example, worked for many years as an associate of Thomas Edison, trying to soften the wax of phonographic cylinders by altering their chemical constitution. Every experiment he tried proved ineffective. Then, after pondering night after night trying to mentally 'cough up' an answer, he tells how it came, "like a flash of lightning. I could not shut waxes out of my mind, even in my sleep," he says, "Suddenly, through headache and daze, I saw the solution."

If such discovery could come out of meditating on a natural object, think what spiritual treasures can come out of meditating on the Word of God. It has been said that, to get the best out of life, great matters have to be given more than a single thought. Meditation is just that — giving biblical truths continuous thought.

Once you have grasped the concept of meditation and know how to apply it, you will find your spirit becoming the secret workshop of an unseen Sculptor, moulding your character development and making your life a radiant testimony to the power and grace of the Lord Jesus Christ.

INSPIRATION AND AUTHORITY OF *The Bible*

GOD'S ANSWERS TO MAN'S QUESTIONS

Look up each of the Bible verses below, then one at a time compare the scriptual answer to the questions listed. See if you can match the answer to the appropriate question and place the relevant letter (A, B, C, etc.) in the box provided. (Answers can be found on page 35).

A. 1 Thess. 2:13   B. Matt. 4:4   C. 2 Tim. 3:16–17   D. Prov. 30:5
E. Matt. 5:17   F. Psalm 138:2   G. 2 Peter 1:21   H. Malachi 3:6

1 Was it man's idea to put together the words of the Bible?	
2 Is every word of the original manuscripts pure and free from error?	
3 Why is it important to read, study and meditate on the Bible regularly?	
4 How highly on God's scale of priorities does He put His Word?	
5 Does God's word change to meet the needs of succeeding generations?	
6 How much of God's Word, the Bible is "God-breathed?"	
7 Did Christ abolish the Old Testament?	
8 Did the Early Church believe in the inspiration of Scripture?	

CONSIDER:

1. What have you learnt about God's Word from reading the above scriptures?

2. Which of these verses do you find most challenging, and why?

RE-ESTABLISHING YOUR *Priorities*

Who, or what, has first place in your life?

Now and again it is important for Christians to examine their priorities.

Is your day built around your time with God or is your time with God built around your day?

Fill in the chart so that you might be able to pinpoint exactly how your time is spent in an **average** week.

	12–5	5–6	6–7	7–8	8–9	9–10	10–11
SUNDAY							
MONDAY							
TUESDAY							
WEDNESDAY							
THURSDAY							
FRIDAY							
SATURDAY							

*"Make the best use of your time,
despite all the evils of these days.
Don't be vague but grasp firmly what you know
to be the will of the Lord"* (Eph. 5:16–17, J.B. Phillips)

The purpose of the chart is to enable you to evaluate the best use of your time.
Fill in the spaces, indicating exactly what you did for each hour period. It is
important to record *what you did,* not what you intended
to do or should have done.

11–12	12–1	1–2	2–3	3–4	4–5	5–6	6–7	7–8	8–9	9–10	10–11	11–12

CONCLUSION:

What do you conclude from this? Are you giving adequate time to
the cultivation and development of your spirit and soul? Make a
note of anything you have to do to re-establish or rearrange your
spiritual priorities.

IN ORDER TO GIVE TIME TO BIBLICAL MEDITATION I MUST:

1. _____

2. _____

3. _____

4. _____

5. _____

3

For meditation to be effective there must be a conviction in the heart that the Bible is the inspired and infallible word of God. Any doubt about this will mean that you will come to some Scriptural passages with a degree of uncertainty about their authority. This will in turn deprive you of the spiritual benefits that result from the art of Biblical Meditation.

It is not the purpose of this manual to defend the Bible or to rebut the arguments of those who claim the Bible contains glaring errors. It is assumed that those seeking to know and understand the principle of Biblical Meditation will already have a conviction that the Bible is true and that it is the final authority for life.

But what does this conviction for life really mean? Ponder the following points and write in the texts.

1. IT MEANS THAT ONE BELIEVES THE BIBLE IS TRUE IN EVERYTHING IT AFFIRMS AND CONTAINS NO ERRORS

Those who set out to discredit the Bible claim that it contains many contradictions and mistakes. But prayerful study of the Scriptures shows that what some people view as contradictions are really only paradoxes. When one approaches the Bible with the assumption that it is truly the Word of God then apparent contradictions are seen in a new light.

(Write text here)

See Psalm 12:6

2. IT MEANS THAT ONE BELIEVES THE BIBLE IS GOD'S MESSAGE TO MAN, NOT MAN'S MESSAGE ABOUT GOD

If the Bible is simply the result of men's efforts and just a collection of interesting writings about God then it cannot be viewed as the final authority for life. The truth is that God, not men, initiated and inspired the Scriptures.

See 2 Peter 1:20-21:   (write text here)

_____

_____

_____

_____

_____

3. IT MEANS THAT ONE BELIEVES GOD WAS NOT RESTRICTED BY THE LIMITATIONS OF MEN AS THEY WROTE THE SCRIPTURES.

Many Bible critics claim that those who contributed to the writing of the Scriptures could not go beyond the limitations of their own understanding or the culture of their day. This theory does not allow for the fact that the Bible is a supernatural revelation and that in its pages God presents His ways and thoughts through the language of men.

See 1 Peter 1:12:   (Write text here)

_____

_____

_____

_____

_____

_____

4. IT MEANS THAT ONE BELIEVES THE BIBLE CAN ONLY BE PROPERLY INTERPRETED WHEN ONE IS INDWELT BY THE HOLY SPIRIT

Only the abiding presence of the Holy Spirit within us enables us to interpret Scripture in the way God meant it to be understood. This explains why many brilliant minds stumble over truths in the Bible which the youngest Christian convert sees with the utmost clarity.

See 1 Corinthians 2:14:   (Write text here)

_____

_____

_____

_____

_____

5. IT MEANS THAT ONE BELIEVES THE BIBLE CONTAINS WORDS AND SAYINGS WHICH WHEN MEDITATED UPON YIELD TREMENDOUS SPIRITUAL POWER.

Our Lord knew Scripture so well that He was able to use it to overcome and defeat Satan in the midst of the great Temptation. Three times he resisted Satan by quoting the precise words that were necessary to rebut the temptation.

This is one of the most important reasons for committing ourselves to the inspiration and authority of the Bible. We can use the precise sayings of Scripture to combat Satan's power and create within us new desires which will be in harmony with God's will and purpose for our lives.

See Ephesians 6:17:   (Write text here)

_____

_____

_____

When you discover how wise and accurate the Bible is and that in addition to helping you know God more intimately it gives you guidance in handling many particular matters you will have greater confidence to study it and meditate upon it.

See if you can match up the biblical answers to the questions below. Look up each reference and check each one against the list of questions. Write the appropriate reference in the space provided beside each question.

Give some time to thinking through how each scripture passage relates to the question.

1. 1 Heb. 12:5–6
2. Luke 16:10
3. 1 Tim. 4:15
4. 1 Pet. 3:14, 4:14
5. Prov. 1:4
6. Matt. 18:15, 1 Pet. 3:9
7. Gal. 6:9
8. Deut. 22:6
9. Prov. 22:24
10. Prov. 22:15, Jer. 17:9
11. Gal. 5:17–18
12. Prov. 18:24
13. Deut. 22:8
14. Heb. 4:12
15. 1 Sam. 15:23

1. What should you do if someone mocks you for doing what you know God wants you to do? _____

2. If someone told you that everyone is born good and is then corrupted by outside influences, what passage would you use to refute that idea? _____

3. Is a Christian entitled to gossip about someone who has harmed them? _____

4. If you find a bird sitting on a nest, what does the Bible say you can and cannot do? _____

5. Why is it sometimes difficult for us to do what God commands? _____

6. How much of God's word must we delight in if we want to be spiritually successful and prosperous? _____

7. If you hire a man to help you build a roof on a house and he falls off, what does the Bible say about your responsibility? _____

8. What does scripture tell us of real friendship? _____

9. What scripture refutes the idea that because the Bible is an old book it cannot possibly have answers for today? _____

10. What does the Bible say about the importance of concentrating on 'little things' that others may think are unimportant? _____

11. What sin is as terrible as the sin of witchcraft (divination)? _____

12. What scripture should we remind ourselves of when discouraged? _____

13. What passage advises us not to form a friendship with an angry person? _____

14. What should we be sure not to do when God seeks to correct us? _____

15. What scripture tells us how to go about getting wisdom? _____

Correct answers to this quiz can be found on page 35.

4

Now that you have a grasp of the underlying reasons why the art and practice of Biblical Meditation is so necessary and important, you are ready to learn how to do it.

How Should We Meditate?

1. SELECT AN APPROPRIATE VERSE OR PASSAGE OF SCRIPTURE

Beginners in meditation will find it more helpful to start by meditating on one phrase or text rather than on a long passage or chapter. Pick a text that tugs at your heart and seems as if it is saying: Please meditate on me.

EXAMPLE:

> *"Man does not live on bread alone, but on every word that comes from the mouth of God."* (Matt. 4:4)

2. SEEK TO UNDERSTAND THE TRUE MEANING OF THE VERSE IN ITS CONTEXT

It has been said that "a verse taken out of its context becomes a pretext". It is possible to wrest a scripture out of its biblical setting and make it mean something entirely different. The verse we have chosen as an example is taken from the account of Christ's temptation in the wilderness. Christ was making the point that it was more important to live by the words of God than to satisfy his physical hunger.

Make sure too that you understand the meaning of every word in the text. If you don't, consult a dictionary or a Bible dictionary.

3. MEMORISE EVERY WORD OF THE TEXT ON WHICH YOU WISH TO MEDITATE

Those who say they have a bad memory and cannot memorise anything are usually people who have not learned the simple principles of memorisation. Study and practise these three basic principles:

a. Read the phrase or text to yourself slowly so that every word sinks in. Do this several times, out loud if you can. Your ears are a vital part of your memory.

b. Underline the key words. This will help you get into the rhythm of a passage. For example: **MAN** DOES NOT **LIVE** ON **BREAD** ALONE **BUT** ON EVERY **WORD** THAT COMES OUT OF THE **MOUTH** OF **GOD.** Now repeat the verse several times emphasising the words that have been printed in bold type.

c. Write out the verse several times. This is a tip that many have found useful when attempting to memorise a Bible passage. Write it out a dozen times and the chances are you will never forget it.

4. VISUALISE AS FAR AS YOU ARE ABLE THE SIGNIFICANCE OF EACH AND EVERY KEY WORD.

EXAMPLE:

"Man" — All mankind, every person. This is a universal principle. Everyone is included.

"Man **shall not**" — a final decree. No one will change it. It is a definte negative.

"Man shall not **live**" — living is more than existing. There is a physical life and a spiritual life. God made us to enjoy the pleasures of life in a relationship with Him.

5. LET THE VERSE GO OUT OF CONSCIOUSNESS AND THEN BRING IT BACK. DO THIS AS OFTEN AS YOU CAN.

The action of letting a text go out of consciousness and then bringing it back helps not only to impress the verse more deeply into your spirit but gives you practice in the art of retrieving a text from your memory. There will be times when you urgently need to reach for a text (for example — a moment of fierce temptation) and the more practice you have of hiding a text in your memory and retrieving it, the more effective your spiritual life will be.

6. USE THE VERSE AS A TALKING POINT WITH GOD

Using our example text you could pray something like this: "O Lord, I am so grateful that You have given me Your Word, which as Job said "is more than my necessary food". Help me to see that, just as I am dependent upon physical nourishment to get through my day, so also I have to depend on Your Word for the spiritual sustenance I need to meet the challenge of day-to-day living."

In this way you are not only deepening your understanding of a text but adding a new dimension to your prayer life.

7. CONSIDER HOW WHAT YOU ARE MEDITATING UPON CAN BE APPLIED TO YOUR LIFE

Those who have had long experience in the art of meditation claim that the more they personalised a verse of Scripture the more impact it had upon them.

EXAMPLE:

"Man shall not **live** . . ."   I don't want just to be alive; I want to to live, really live. This means that I must let God live His life through me. I must consider how I can let Him see through my eyes, speak through my lips, love through my heart, work through my hands."

". . . by bread **alone** . . ."   If I am to have God's life, I must make sure that I pay more attention to my spiritual diet than my physical diet. Food is important but God's Word is even more important. How can I get more of it?

". . . but by every **word** . . ."   Every word? If every word is so vital and important to my spiritual health — how many do I know? I wish I had started meditating on God's Word before now, but better late than never. I must make it a top priority to get to know God's Word better."

8. QUOTE THE VERSE TO YOURSELF AS YOU GO TO SLEEP AND DO IT AGAIN AS SOON AS YOU AWAKEN

The last thought on your mind before you go to sleep will drop down into your unconscious and be active there during the hours of the night. Scientists tell us that the unconscious part of our mind goes on working while we are asleep. If that is so then let it work on the Word of God.

Repeating the verse when you awake in the morning will serve to impress it even more deeply into your inner being.

Keys to Remembering

"Do not let this book of the Law depart from your mouth; meditate on it day and night, so that you may be careful to do everything written in it. Then you will be prosperous and successful." (Joshua 1:8)

It would be possible to be able to quote the entire New Testament word for word and not have one word of God's Word in your heart. An unbelieving school teacher can quote the words of the Bible. The devil can quote the Bible, but you could hardly say he has God's Word in his heart.

God said in Deuteronomy 11:18, "Fix these words of mine in your hearts and minds." But how do you get it from your head into your heart? You do it by meditating on it, by talking to Jesus about it, by experiencing it in your daily life. Take steps to make it a part of you, not just knowledge in your head.

Understanding that you should memorise and knowing that it should be in your heart, you are now faced with the question most asked, "How do I do it?"

To record something in your memory, you need an image. When I say the word "elephant" to you, does your mind see an image of some kind? How about "rose"? And "sports car"? When you thought of a sports car, did it have a colour on it? Now when I say the word "justification" do you see an image? How about "grace" or "faith"?

The mind functions with images. It needs pictures and likenesses to make the lasting impression it needs to be able to recall. Jesus knew this. That is one of the reasons He always used parables when He taught ". . . He did not say anything to them without using a parable" (Matt. 13:34). Why? Because He knew spiritual truths and thoughts need to have a physical likeness to be remembered. The word parable means "to throw or lay beside; to compare". It signifies the placing of one thing beside another for the purposes of comparing, understanding and remembering.

This ability to form images is very important to memory. Don't overlook it because it is simple. Practice making images by visualising the 23rd Psalm as the Psalmist described it. See the pasture, the water, the rod, and the staff. See the picture.

Once learned, the words of Scripture need to be retained. "Teach them to your children" (Deut. 11:19). The word "teach" here means to do a thing again and again as in the whetting or sharpening of an instrument. Your mind forgets what it does not consider important. Repetition and review will keep what you have learned fresh in your mind. If you never review at all, you will forget. That is not because you have a poor memory. It is because you have by your own actions told your mind, "This is not important, get rid of it".

Dick Scott

When Should We Meditate?

Before examining the best times to meditate some thought must given to the fact that there are clearly times when we should not meditate. A Christian pilot for example would be acting irresponsibly if when bringing his plane in to land manually he decided to spend a few minutes meditating. Those involved in tasks where the safety of others depends on their fullest concentration should not during their working hours give their minds to meditation.

Scripture suggests four occasions when meditation is the most profitable: Deuteronomy 6:7 & Psalm 63:5-6.

1. "WHEN YOU SIT IN YOUR HOUSE . . ." This means during times of leisure and relaxation.

2. "WHEN YOU WALK BY THE WAY . . ." This means when you go out for a walk or even on your way to and from work.

3. "WHEN YOU LIE DOWN . . ." As you lay down to sleep at night.

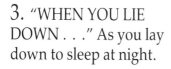

4. "WHEN YOU AWAKE." When you awake in the morning.

MEDITATE ON PSALM 1

You are about to start your first meditation assignment. Before proceeding to this, you should read through the eight principles that we have outlined once more, in order to be clear in your own mind about what you should be seeking to do.

Now you can begin to put the eight principles into effect by meditating on Psalm 1.

Be sure to fill in your thoughts and observations as they come to you . . .

1. BLESSED IS THE MAN WHO WALKS NOT IN THE COUNSEL OF THE UNGODLY . . .

(Thoughts and comments) ———————————————

_____

_____

_____

_____

_____

2. NOR STANDS IN THE PATH OF SINNERS . . .

_____

_____

_____

_____

3. NOR SITS IN THE SEAT OF THE SCORNFUL

_____

_____

_____

_____

4. BUT HIS DELIGHT IS IN THE LAW OF THE LORD . . .

_____

_____

_____

_____

_____

5. AND IN HIS LAW HE MEDITATES DAY AND NIGHT . . .

_____

_____

_____

_____

_____

_____

6. HE SHALL BE LIKE A TREE PLANTED BY THE RIVERS OF LIVING WATER . . .

_____

_____

_____

_____

_____

_____

7. THAT BRINGS FORTH ITS FRUIT IN ITS SEASON . . .

_____

_____

_____

_____

_____

8. WHOSE LEAF ALSO SHALL NOT WITHER . . .

_____

_____

_____

_____

9. THAT WHATSOEVER HE DOES SHALL PROSPER . . .

_____

_____

_____

_____

_____

10. THE UNGODLY ARE NOT SO BUT ARE LIKE THE CHAFF WHICH THE WIND DRIVES AWAY . . .

_____

_____

_____

_____

_____

11. THEREFORE THE UNGODLY SHALL NOT STAND IN THE JUDGMENT . . .

_____

_____

_____

_____

_____

12. NOR SINNERS IN THE CONGREGATION OF THE RIGHTEOUS . . .

_____

_____

_____

_____

_____

_____

13. FOR THE LORD KNOWS THE WAY OF THE RIGHTEOUS . . .

_____

_____

_____

_____

_____

_____

14. BUT THE WAY OF THE UNGODLY SHALL PERISH . . .

_____

_____

_____

_____

_____

Now that you have completed your first meditation assignment, take a few moments to consider the things about which God has spoken to you. What special encouragements and challenges have you had?

_____

_____

_____

Further meditation assignments can be found at the back of this manual.

5

THE Rewards OF MEDITATION

Countless benefits flow from the effort we make to meditate in the Scriptures. Consider just five of these important benefits.

Look up the Scriptural reference in each case, write it in and then proceed to MEMORISE and MEDITATE on it.

1. SUCCESS

The book of Joshua narrates the story of how a man of proven character and ability led a nation of several million people across the flood-swollen Jordan — to settle in the Promised Land. During the seven-year period covered by the book of Joshua the 12 tribes of Israel met and defeated a total of 31 armies and captured 20 cities. The secret of Joshua's outstanding success lay largely in the fact that he knew how to meditate.

As Joshua meditated on God's word the continuous mental and spiritual discipline produced in him clarity of thought, sharpness of intellect and greater power of concentration.

Joshua 1:8: _____

_____

_____

_____

_____

_____

2. UNDERSTANDING

The world gains an understanding about life from observation, learning and experience. However, much of the knowledge in today's world is based on humanistic assumptions and is often at variance with God's eternal principles. A Christian who meditates in the Scriptures will experience an understanding of life which cannot be comprehended by even the most brilliant of minds.

Psalm 119:99 _____

_____

_____

3. A KEENER SENSE OF THE DIFFERENCE BETWEEN RIGHT AND WRONG

The ability to discern the difference between right and wrong is one of the most important qualities a Christian can possess and can be experienced in even greater measure through the power of Biblical Meditation. This ability is implanted in us at the time of our conversion to Christ but it must be cultivated and developed by the continuous inner activity of meditation.

When we read and meditate upon the Word of God, the Almighty uses the Word hidden in our hearts to show us when our thoughts, actions and attitudes are displeasing to Him.

Psalm 119:11 _____

_____

_____

4. SPIRITUAL FRUITFULNESS

A major reason why so many Christian lives are barren and unfruitful is because they have never learned the joys of meditation. We saw in Psalm 1 that God promises that the person who meditates in his law day and night will become like a tree planted by the river that brings forth fruit in its season — and whose leaves never wither. Jesus promised us also that when we allow His word to abide in our hearts we will "bear much fruit".

John 15:7-8 _____

_____

_____

_____

_____

5. WE DISCOVER HOW TO LIVE

One of the great tragedies of these days is that we know almost everything about life — except how to live it. The truth is however that no matter what other exercises we as Christians engage in — worship, prayer, evangelism, Bible study and so on — we can never expect to reach the heights of abundant living until we know how to meditate in the Scriptures.

When we meditate in the Bible we experience a heightening of all our powers, enabling us to enjoy and experience a quality of life which is divine. The mind becomes clearer, the emotions become more balanced and co-ordinated, and the will becomes more active and decisive. We become experts in the art of living only as we meditate on God's Word and keep His commandments.

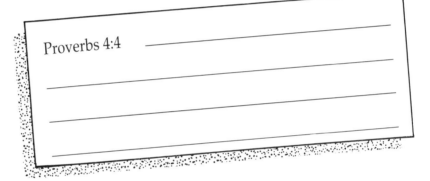

Proverbs 4:4 _____

Cleanse and Build

One day a family living on the edge of a desert was amazed to see that seeds had sprouted in the salty desert sands behind their home. No-one could understand how this had happened since they had tried to cultivate vegetables and flowers with no positive results.

The mystery was solved when someone discovered that every day the mother had thrown her dish water out of the back door. After months and months of this process, the salt, which hindered growth, had been washed out of the sand. One day she threw away some seeds and as they fell in the place where the water had washed the salt from the soil, they began to sprout and grow.

In the same way, as we saturate our minds with God's Word, it will wash out thoughts opposed to Scripture and will reconstruct other ideas around God's principles . . . "cleansing her (the Church) by the washing with water through the word" (Eph. 5:26).

"Wherefore lay apart all filthiness . . . and receive with meekness the engrafted word which is able to save your souls."

(James 1:21, KJV)

In horticulture it is possible to take a shoot, a bud, or even a branch, and unite it with an established plant until the two separate parts grow together to form one plant. Just as branches can be grafted into a tree and bear new fruit, so we can 'graft' God's Word into our heart and produce spiritual qualities and characteristics that enrich our personalities. As we continually meditate on verses of Scripture, so God's truth becomes a part of our lives. We become one with God's Word and exhibit the resultant fruit and lifestyle.

For example:

If we engraft 1 Corinthians 13 into our hearts
we will develop . . .

more genuine love.

___

If we engraft 1 Peter 1:1-9 into our hearts
we will develop . . .

greater patience in time of suffering.

___

If we engraft Romans 6 & 8 into our hearts
we will have . . .

greater victory over sin.

Don't be tempted to skip over this page for it is only as you grasp the principle of engrafting that you will be motivated to make Biblical Meditation work for you.

___

It is not necessary to look up these scriptures now, but if they refer to an area in your life in which you would like to be more fruitful, make time soon to meditate upon these passages.

*Think about the
principle of engrafting
for a little while . . .*

WRITE OUT YOUR OWN
DEFINITION OF THE TERM

'Engrafting' is

_____

_____

_____

_____

_____

MEDITATE FOR A *Change in Your Life*

Through meditation you can engraft the Word of God into your life and bring about major character changes in your personality. Look down the list of character qualities below and select just one quality that you would like to work on as a priority in the very near future. Applying the principles you have learned in this manual, you should begin to meditate on the appropriate Scripture passage that is linked to that quality. A Reference or 'margin' Bible will give you additional scriptures on which to focus.

Spend at least a week focusing on the passage related to your selected character quality and then move on to the next in order of priority.

As you approach this section, keep in mind what was said on the opening page: that we benefit from meditation in the Scriptures only as we are willing to be obedient to them. Make sure, therefore, that any known wrongs in your life are dealt with and then you are in a position to let "the word . . . have free course and be glorified" (2 Thess. 3:1, NKJ).

Note: The first Scripture listed focuses on a text or passage and the second shows how the text is illustrated in the life of a Bible character.

Caution: Don't work on more than one quality at a time. Spiritual growth takes a while to develop. Remember the Christian life is a **walk**, not a mad dash (see Matt. 6:28).

CHARACTER QUALITY TO BE DEVELOPED	SCRIPTURE TO BE ENGRAFTED
☐ **ALERTNESS** The ability to respond rightly to what is happening around you	Mark 14:38 Acts 23:12-16
☐ **BOLDNESS** The confidence to do what you know God wants you to do	Acts 4:29 1 Sam. 17:45
☐ **COMPASSION** The desire to help heal the hurts and suffering of others	1 John 3:17 Luke 10:33-35
☐ **DETERMINATION** The purposeful pursuit of right goals	Isaiah 50:7 Luke 9:51

☐ **ENDURANCE** The ability to withstand inward stress — **2 Tim. 2:3** / **2 Cor. 4:7-11**

☐ **FAITH** The confidence that God will always keep His word — **Heb. 11:1** / **Acts 27:25**

☐ **GENEROSITY** The quality of giving freely and magnanimously — **Luke 6:38** / **John 12:1-8**

☐ **HUMILITY** The attitude that has a 'stoop' in it — **Phil. 2:5-11** / **John 13:1-17**

☐ **INITIATIVE** The ability to see what needs to be done without being told — **Prov. 13:16** / **Esther 4:1-17**

☐ **JOYFULNESS** The exultation of one's inner being — **Psalm 16:11** / **Jer. 15:16**

☐ **KINDNESS** The gentle consideration of others — **Eph. 4:32** / **Luke 10:33**

☐ **LOVE** The bringing about of the highest good in the life of another — **1 Cor. 13:4-8** / **2 Sam. 1:26**

☐ **MEEKNESS** The willingness to submit all personal rights and expectations to God — **Psalm 62:5** / **Matt. 26:39**

☐ **NEATNESS** The quality of being tidy and methodical — **1 Cor. 14:40** / **John 20:6-7**

☐ **OBEDIENCE** The willingness to do what God asks irrespective of feelings — 1 Sam. 15:22 / Heb. 11:8

☐ **PATIENCE** The capacity to accept difficult situations without giving God a deadline to remove it — James 1:2-4 / 2 Cor. 12:7-10

☐ **RESOURCEFULNESS** The wise and proper use of things others might disregard — Luke 16:10 / Gen. 41:46-49, 53-56

☐ **SENSITIVITY** The awareness of what is going on in the emotional spectrum of others — Rom. 12:15 / John 11:35

☐ **TRUTHFULNESS** The quality of being honest and avoiding all forms of deception — Eph. 4:25 / Matt. 26:63-64

☐ **UNDERSTANDING** The ability to grasp what God is saying — Eph. 5:17 / Gal. 1:15-16

☐ **VIRTUE** The moral excellence that radiates from a person who obeys God's word — 2 Peter 1:5 / Ruth 3:11

☐ **WISDOM** The ability to use knowledge to the most purposeful end — Prov. 9:10 / 1 Kings 3:16-28

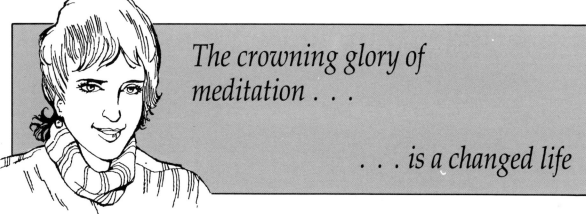

The crowning glory of meditation . . .

. . . is a changed life

TAKE THIS FINAL TEST

TRUE or FALSE

1. Biblical Meditation is actively putting the mind into a state of relaxation.　____ ____

2. Biblical Meditation begins when we turn our thoughts toward God.　____ ____

3. A guaranteed way of getting a peaceful night's sleep is to meditate on God's Word.　____ ____

4. Biblical Meditation enhances the study of the Bible by ensuring that the word becomes 'flesh' — in us.　____ ____

5. A major difference between TM and Biblical Meditation is that TM focuses on emptying the mind while Biblical Meditation focuses on filling it with the Word of God.　____ ____

6. Biblical Meditation helps a person develop dependency on their own inner resources.　____ ____

7. Biblical Meditation assists a person in developing spiritual sensitivity and awareness.　____ ____

8. A good way to begin learning the art of Biblical Meditation is to memorise a whole chapter and then focus on it verse by verse.　____ ____

9. The Bible says there are three key periods in a day when we can meditate.　____ ____

10. The principle of 'engrafting' can be employed by any Christian at any time and with no prerequirements.　____ ____

ANSWERS TO QUIZ
PAGE 9

1.G; **2.**D; **3.**B; **4.**F;
5.H; **6.**C; **7.**E; **8.**A.

ANSWERS TO QUIZ
PAGES 15 – 16

1. 1 Peter 3:14 & 4:14.
2. Prov. 22:15 & Jer. 17:9
3. Matt. 18:15 & 1 Peter 3:9.
4. Deut. 22:6
5. Gal. 5:17-18
6. 1 Tim. 4:15
7. Deut. 22:8
8. Prov. 18:24
9. Heb. 4:12
10. Luke 16:10
11. 1 Sam. 15:23
12. Gal. 6:9
13. Prov. 22:24
14. Heb. 12:5-6
15. Prov. 1:4

ANSWERS TO FINAL
TEST PAGE 34

1. **False:** Meditation is an activity — engaging the mind and spirit with the content of God's eternal word.
2. **False.** Meditation is not thinking our thoughts about God but thinking His thoughts after him.
3. **False.** Meditation may help us to sleep peacefully but at first it may dislodge impure thoughts which are entrenched in our minds. This can cause unpleasant dreams which may continue until our minds are purified by the word of God.
4. **True.**
5. **True.**
6. **False.** The more we meditate on God's word the more we will come to see the importance of depending upon God rather than upon our own strength and ideas.
7. **True.**
8. **False.** Beginners should start with a single text not a whole chapter. You cannot learn to run until you have learned to walk.
9. **False.** It says there are four (see Deut. 6:7).
10. **False.** We are instructed to "lay apart all filthiness and superfluity of naughtiness before receiving the engrafted word which is able to save our souls." (see James 1:21, KJV).

Thought and Discussion

1. How has your own understanding of meditation changed while following this course?

2. What benefits have you received from the assignments you have already undertaken?

3. How will you seek to apply the principles of meditation in your study of God's Word in the future?

6

Going on . . .

Although you have nearly reached the end page of this manual, this is not intended to be "the end" but rather the beginning of an approach to Biblical Meditation which we hope you will follow through, and profit by, for the rest of your life.

Continue to apply the basic principles you have been learning. Here are some suggestions:

☐ After you have used the *Further Meditation Assignments* in this manual, select other passages on which to meditate phrase by phrase in the same way.

☐ Note from your daily Bible readings other passages to go back over in meditation.

☐ Share what you have been learning with someone else and introduce them to this manual.

☐ Discuss the subject with your minister and introduce him to the manual! The principles enunciated here can be demonstrated in preaching.

☐ Don't put away this manual now and forget it. Every so often go back to it and give yourself a refresher course!

Now that you have worked through this manual you may want to form a group to encourage other people to understand the benefits of Biblical meditation. If this is the case, please refer to the 'Points for Leaders' (page 48), which will show you the best way to prepare for this.

Assignment 1

MEDITATE ON ROMANS 8:38–39

1. FOR I AM CONVINCED THAT NEITHER DEATH NOR LIFE . . .

(Thoughts and comments) _____

_____

_____

_____

2. NEITHER ANGELS NOR DEMONS . . .

_____

_____

_____

_____

3. NEITHER THE PRESENT NOR THE FUTURE . . .

_____

_____

_____

_____

_____

4. NOR ANY POWERS . . .

_____

_____

_____

5. NEITHER HEIGHT NOR DEPTH . . .

_____

_____

_____

_____

6. NOR ANYTHING ELSE IN ALL CREATION . . .

_____

_____

_____

_____

7. WILL BE ABLE TO SEPARATE US . . .

_____

_____

_____

_____

8. FROM THE LOVE OF GOD THAT IS IN CHRIST JESUS OUR LORD.

_____

_____

_____

_____

_____

Assignment 2

MEDITATE ON COLOSSIANS 3:12–17

1. THEREFORE, AS GOD'S CHOSEN PEOPLE . . .

(Thoughts and comments) _____

_____

_____

_____

2. HOLY AND DEARLY LOVED . . .

_____

_____

_____

_____

3. CLOTHE YOURSELVES WITH COMPASSION . . .

_____

_____

_____

_____

4. KINDNESS, HUMILITY, GENTLENESS, AND PATIENCE . . .

_____

_____

_____

_____

5. BEAR WITH EACH OTHER AND FORGIVE WHATEVER GRIEVANCES YOU MAY HAVE AGAINST ONE ANOTHER . . .

_____

_____

_____

_____

6. FORGIVE AS THE LORD FORGAVE YOU . . .

_____

_____

_____

_____

7. AND OVER ALL THESE VIRTUES PUT ON LOVE, WHICH BINDS THEM ALL TOGETHER IN PERFECT UNITY . . .

_____

_____

_____

_____

8. LET THE PEACE OF CHRIST RULE IN YOUR HEARTS, SINCE AS MEMBERS OF ONE BODY YOU WERE CALLED TO PEACE . . .

_____

_____

_____

_____

9. AND BE THANKFUL . . .

_____

_____

_____

10. LET THE WORD OF CHRIST DWELL IN YOU RICHLY AS YOU TEACH AND ADMONISH ONE ANOTHER WITH ALL WISDOM . . .

_____

_____

_____

_____

_____

11. AND AS YOU SING PSALMS, HYMNS AND SPIRITUAL SONGS . . .

_____

_____

_____

12. WITH GRATITUDE IN YOUR HEARTS TO GOD . . .

_____

_____

_____

13. AND WHATEVER YOU DO, WHETHER IN WORD OR DEED, DO IT ALL IN THE NAME OF THE LORD JESUS . . .

_____

_____

_____

_____

14. GIVING THANKS TO GOD THE FATHER THROUGH HIM.

_____

_____

_____

Assignment 3

MEDITATE ON 1 JOHN 4:7–11

1. DEAR FRIENDS, LET US LOVE ONE ANOTHER, FOR LOVE COMES FROM GOD . . .

(Thoughts and comments) _____

_____

_____

_____

2. EVERYONE WHO LOVES HAS BEEN BORN OF GOD AND KNOWS GOD . . .

_____

_____

_____

_____

3. WHOEVER DOES NOT LOVE DOES NOT KNOW GOD, BECAUSE GOD IS LOVE . . .

_____

_____

_____

_____

4. THIS IS HOW GOD SHOWED HIS LOVE AMONG US: HE SENT HIS ONE AND ONLY SON INTO THE WORLD . . .

_____

_____

_____

5. THAT WE MIGHT LIVE THROUGH HIM . . .

_____

_____

_____

_____

6. THIS IS LOVE: NOT THAT WE LOVED GOD, BUT THAT HE LOVED US . . .

_____

_____

_____

_____

_____

_____

7. AND SENT HIS SON AS AN ATONING SACRIFICE FOR OUR SINS . . .

_____

_____

_____

_____

_____

8. DEAR FRIENDS, SINCE GOD SO LOVED US, WE ALSO OUGHT TO LOVE ONE ANOTHER.

_____

_____

_____

Assignment 4

MEDITATE ON REVELATION 1:5b–8

1. TO HIM WHO LOVES US AND HAS FREED US FROM OUR SINS BY HIS BLOOD . . .

_____

_____

_____

_____

2. AND HAS MADE US TO BE A KINGDOM AND PRIESTS TO SERVE HIS GOD AND FATHER . . .

_____

_____

_____

_____

_____

3. TO HIM BE GLORY AND POWER FOR EVER AND EVER! AMEN . . .

_____

_____

_____

_____

4. LOOK, HE IS COMING WITH THE CLOUDS, AND EVERY EYE WILL SEE HIM . . .

_____

_____

_____

5. EVEN THOSE WHO PIERCED HIM . . .

_____

_____

_____

_____

6. AND ALL THE PEOPLES OF THE EARTH WILL MOURN BECAUSE OF HIM. SO SHALL IT BE! AMEN . . .

_____

_____

_____

_____

7. "I AM THE ALPHA AND THE OMEGA," SAYS THE LORD GOD . . .

_____

_____

_____

_____

8. "WHO IS, AND WHO WAS, AND WHO IS TO COME, THE ALMIGHTY."

_____

_____

_____

_____

NOTES

OTHER CWR PUBLICATIONS

Daily Bible reading devotionals

Every Day with Jesus

Written by Selwyn Hughes, each edition focuses on a theme to promote greater closeness to God and effectiveness in the world.

Young People's Every Day with Jesus

Encouraging daily notes open the Bible and relate it to the lives of 12-16s. Brightly illustrated with lots of relevant news and features.

Topz

Topz makes use of the cartoon adventures of the Topz Gang, puzzles and activities to introduce 7-11s to God's love and His Word.

All three titles published bi-monthly.

Early Days with Jesus

Six undated activity books for 3-6s to learn of God's love for them.

See, Love, Follow

by Eddie Tait

Takes a fresh look at what the Bible says about the Christian life, the Church and our part in it. *See, Love, Follow* is a six-week course with weekly points for discussion. Ideal for Bible studies, discipleship classes and Lent groups.

The Divine Eagle

by Selwyn Hughes

From time to time God overturns our familiar worlds to move us to a deeper faith and dependence on Him. Selwyn shows how God seeks to use these experiences to move us towards His highest purposes for our lives. Illustrated with four colour watercolour drawings.

The Divine Gardener

by Selwyn Hughes

Focuses on Scriptures portraying God as the divine gardener who prunes and shapes our lives to produce greater fruit and effectiveness. With four colour illustrations.

The Life of Christ

every day through one year

by Trevor Partridge, Rita and Neil McLaughlan

Read through the life of Jesus day by day in a year. A chronological running commentary that illuminates the events of our Lord's life and pinpoints the adventure of living for Jesus today. Illustrated.

For a brochure detailing all CWR's current publications, please write to:
CWR, 10 Brooklands Close, Sunbury-on-Thames, Middx., TW16 7DX, or to your National Distributor.

Points for Leaders

This manual lends itself to group study, as well as individual use. If you are a leader planning to take a number of people through the manual, you should be mindful of the following:

1. You will need to work through each section yourself, applying the principles to your own life. Then you should work through it again before the group meets, planning sessions for the group. This will help you to become familiar with the contents and anticipate any questions that might arise.

2. Each section has been designed to last approximately 60 minutes. Encourage the members of the group not to rush through each part of a particular section. As with meditation itself, this study will only be of real value if time is given to consider the contents carefully.

3. After each exercise, encourage group members to share their thoughts and discoveries.

4. It is important that you keep to the outline of the manual. It has been designed to lead people step by step along a path of discovery and growing awareness of the value of Biblical meditation. Additional material may detract from the goal of each section.

5. Try to meet somewhere quiet as a group, where the group as a whole, or individual members of it, will not be disturbed.

6. You may wish to finish each section with a time of thanksgiving, and if practical, praise and worship, thanking God for what He has revealed, encouraging each group member to participate.

7. Teaching others can often lead to a chain reaction. Encourage group members who seem to have grasped the principles outlined in the manual to teach others in turn. Further groups may result.